# ROUGH DRAFTS
## AN ACTIVITY BOOK
*Kathleen Shine Cain*

# SIMON & SCHUSTER HANDBOOK FOR WRITERS

*Lynn Quitman Troyka*

**FIFTH EDITION**

D1401229

PRENTICE HALL, *Upper Saddle River, NJ 07458*

© 1999 by PRENTICE-HALL, INC.
Simon & Schuster / A Viacom Company
Upper Saddle River, New Jersey 07458

10 9 8 7 6 5 4 3 2 1

**ISBN 0-13-081648-5**
Printed in the United States of America

# Contents

# Contents

Contents

# Preface

This workbook is designed to provide students with practice in composing, revising, and editing rough drafts. Part I offers students the opportunity to try out various strategies for generating ideas for essays (e.g., grouped lists, freewriting, random sentences), Part II offers them drafts of essays to revise with particular considerations in mind (e.g., organization, audience awareness, support), and Parts III through VI present paragraphs in need of revision and editing for particular problems (e.g., pronoun reference and case, apostrophe, and spelling/hyphenation). The exercises are keyed to appropriate chapters in the second edition of the *Simon & Schuster Handbook,* so that students may refer to the handbook if they encounter difficulty in revising or editing. Exercises in Parts II through VI call for students to make necessary corrections in the workbook, and then to write out the entire revision on a separate sheet of paper. This two-step revision process most closely resembles the process writers use in revising their own work; thus it should reinforce the revision techniques covered in the exercises.

I would like to thank Lynn Quitman Troyka for giving me the opportunity to contribute to the *Simon & Schuster Handbook* package; her help and support over the past several years has given new meaning to the word "mentor." I would also like to thank Martha Masterson and Barbara Reilly of Prentice Hall for their advice and support. And finally, I would like to extend heartfelt thanks to Shannon, who gave up many a summer "field trip" so that mom could get on with her work. I owe you one, kiddo.

PART I           PREWRITING
                    (*S & S* Handbook Chapter 2)

The exercises in this section are designed to provide practice in one of the most difficult writing tasks: generating ideas, or "getting started." There are many ways to begin the writing process; these exercises highlight three of those ways. After practicing each technique, you may be able to determine which works best for your own writing process.

## Exercise 1: Generating Random Lists

Sometimes the easiest way to get started with an assignment is to make a list of everything that comes to mind when you think about the topic. Assume that your assignment is to write a paper on American eating habits. Choose one of the following related topics, and generate a list of fifteen to twenty items on your chosen topic.

eating habits of young adults

fad diets

eating disorders

the family dinner

fast food

ethnic foods

the gourmet revolution

airline (or cafeteria) food

## Exercise 2:  Developing Grouped Lists

After generating a random list, the next step is to find patterns and
similar ideas. Look at your random list, and group similar items into
categories.  Items that do not fit into any group can be set aside, and
may later be dropped entirely.  When you look at your groups,  you
may discover that you have a good deal to say about one aspect of the
topic; mark off those items with an asterisk.

## Exercise 3: Freewriting

**Some writers find that they can generate ideas by freewriting, or writing whatever comes to mind without stopping to consider such things as style, grammar, and spelling. Assume that your assignment is to write a paper about public figures. Choose one of the following topics, and freewrite for ten to fifteen minutes on your chosen topic. Remember not to stop, review, or cross out.**

| | |
|---|---|
| sports stars | musicians |
| actors | business leaders |
| elected officials | authors |
| religious leaders | artists |

Exercise 4: Focused Freewriting

Frequently freewriting produces a number of interesting ideas. Review your freewriting, and find an idea, a word, a phrase, or a sentence that you might focus on to develop ideas for a paper. Using that focus, write down as many related thoughts as you can. Keep your topic in mind and keep the ten- to fifteen-minute time limit.

## Exercise 5: Writing Down Random Sentences

Some writers find it easier to begin by actually writing a sort of "pre" rough draft, a series of random sentences on the topic at hand. This method is similar to generating lists in that it involves writing down ideas related to the assignment, and it is like freewriting in that the writer goes beyond listing items and actually completes many thoughts on the topic. It differs from the other two methods in that the writer thinks about relationships between ideas and tries to compose complete, related sentences. Assume that your assignment is to write a paper about tourist attractions. Choose one of the following topics, and write a series of random sentences on your chosen topic.

amusement parks

natural wonders

museums

sporting events

theme parks

historical sites

great cities

cultural attractions

## Exercise 6: Ordering Random Sentences

Once written, random sentences usually suggest some sort of order. Review your sentences, and arrange them in an order that will help you develop a paper on the topic.

## PART II

WRITING AND REVISING ESSAYS
                (*S & S* Handbook Chapters 1-6, 34, 35, 37)


Once a writer has a rough draft to work with, specific considerations arise. In addition to the subject of the paper, audience and purpose are also important. Such issues as organization and coherence, relationship between writer and reader, and support and documentation of sources must be considered as the writer revises. The following exercises cover particular areas of concern in revision. Each draft is written with a specific purpose, and revision will focus on an area of concern directly related to that purpose. During this stage of revision, issues of sentence structure, grammar, and mechanics are set aside for the moment while the writer focuses on the primary issue of getting the message across to the reader. (Revising for sentence structure, grammar, and mechanics will be dealt with later.) With the exception of the research paper, each of the following exercises includes a draft with final comments from an instructor, focusing on one area of revision. Using those comments (and, when appropriate, referring to underlined sections in the draft itself), revise the drafts, first by making appropriate changes on the drafts themselves, and then by rewriting the essay. For the research paper, use the student's own notes as guides for revision.

**Focusing on the underlined sections, and without changing the paper
significantly, revise the following draft in order to present a consistent
tone. (Decide upon tone by considering the overall impression created
by the writer.)**


Gloria: The Hurricane that Almost Was


The weather reports began to warn us of her visit on Tuesday. At least three
times during the six-o'clock news the weather map filled the screen, with arrows
pointing to that swirling mass of clouds over the coast of South Carolina. We were
way up at the top of the map, but, the weatherman told us, by Friday that mass of
clouds would <u>be messing with</u> New England as well. Hurricane Gloria was on her
way.


By Wednesday afternoon <u>retailers who specialized in food staples and items
essential for survival found themselves beseiged by flocks of anxiety-ridden patrons
eager to provide themselves with the necessary provisions for a period of severely
inclement weather.</u> People from rural areas, where water was pumped from
individual wells by electricity, were buying bottled water by the case. No candles
could be found in any stores for miles around, and batteries were fetching premium
prices. I remember deciding to stop to pick up a few things for dinner on Wednesday
after work. What was going on at Mel's Market? I could not find a parking space in
the usually half-empty lot, and when I finally parked down the street and walked up

to the store, I could not get a shopping cart. <u>The stock in the canned goods section was severely depleted, and the situation was similar in the sections devoted to bread, snacks, and soda.</u> Deciding that a fried chicken dinner was not worth the half-hour wait in the checkout line, I headed home for pot luck.

On Thursday huge X's made of masking tape began to appear on windows everywhere. Lawns looked desolate, stripped of their patio furniture, bird baths, and badminton nets. Television antennas were being removed from the roofs of houses in the un-cabled sections of town. And <u>in all locations citizens were conversing about hurricanes.</u> My neighbors reminisced about Hurricane Carol in '53, when huge plate-glass windows were blown out of department stores and centuries-old trees were torn out by their roots, pulling up with them half-acres of dirt. One of the secretaries at work recalled Agnes, who in '72 flooded roads with three feet of murky water. Others who hadn't been lucky enough to live through their own hurricane talked about news stories of storms with names like Camille and Diane. The talk was exciting, but frightening too: <u>Camille left in her wake the utmost tragedy, taking over six hundred lives of helpless men, women, and children along the gulf coast before she weakened; other storms, not so powerful as Camille, destroyed ancestral homes and left countless maimed, broken bodies behind in their raging fury.</u> As the hour of Gloria's arrival grew near, excitement turned to apprehension.

Friday morning dawned clear and bright, with no sign of the impending storm anywhere. But the AM radio stations had all turned themselves over to the "storm desks" usually reserved for blizzards in the dead of winter. Word was that we could expect Gloria by noon. As the skies darkened and the air became still, <u>my boss said we could all knock off early on account of the storm</u>. The drive home was like a ride through a ghost town: downtown was deserted, and homes looked like bunkers waiting for an armed assault. I had just pulled in the driveway when the first winds came up, blowing a few early-fall leaves into a miniature tornado before gently depositing them on the hood of my car. Then the rain began, softly at first, <u>but then it really came down in buckets.</u> As the storm grew louder the power went out, and we relied on a battery-operated radio to bring us news. Gloria was here.

By noon there was quite a wind; small branches were being blown off trees and a few odd pails and shovels that had been abandoned in neighborhood sandboxes were doing cartwheels across the lawn. But this was no worse than a bad thunderstorm. Where was the hurricane?

It still had not arrived by three, when the forecasters had predicted the worst winds. Nor was there any change at four, or five, or six. Around seven <u>a representative gathering of neighbors assembled in our dining room</u> for cold cuts by candlelight. The talk was of the storm, or rather the non-storm. Here it was, almost eight o'clock, and still there was no sign of a real hurricane. By nine the wind had stopped, and by ten the rain was over too, and we still had not seen anything wild. We all crashed at about midnight, really bummed that there wasn't any good stuff to see. What was with this storm anyway?

The next morning, as the sun shone brightly on the debris in our yard, we began to tidy up. The news reporters were all talking about how lucky it was for us that the hurricane had veered east just before it reached New England. But I wondered. I had watched the preparations all week, and had waited for the momentous event with a mixture of fear and excitement. But Gloria decided at the last minute to wimp out on us. What a bummer! Maybe we were not important enough for her attentions, or maybe she had decided to spare us her fury. Whatever the reason, I have to admit that my primary reaction was disillusionment: I had paid for the performance of the season and it had been cancelled.

*This draft is informative and well organized, and contains vivid details to keep the reader's attention. Personalizing the hurricane and referring to her "visit" are especially effective. The tone, however, is inconsistent: at times quite formal ("A representative gathering of neighbors"), at times quite informal ("What a bummer!"). Several sections also seem far more serious than the rest of the paper (the tragedy of Camille, for example). A more consistent tone would improve the effectiveness of the essay considerably. Sections that need attention are underlined.*

**Exercise 2: The Descriptive Essay--Revising for Organization**
**(*S & S* Handbook Chapter 3c)**

**Focusing on the end comment, revise the following draft by rearranging material in a way that provides consistent organization.**

Calendars

While searching through some old boxes in my mother's attic the other day, I came upon a calendar from 1965. The pictures were of serene landscapes, with snowcovered mountains and fields for the winter months, green meadows and blue lakes for the summer, budding trees for spring and blazing foliage for fall. Just below the photos was an inscription that read "J. Daniels Agency, Serving all your Insurance Needs." Thinking back, I vaguely remembered seeing such calendars on the wall over our kitchen table when I was a child. Not only would there be a wall calendar from the insurance agent, but another from the local service station (graced with photos of sleek, shiny automobiles), and a little desk calendar (no pictures) from the grocery store. In almost every room of the house you could find a calendar from a local establishment. They came every Christmas, gifts from those who appreciated our service during the year.

What happened to those calendars of my youth? As I look around the house today, I see on the kitchen wall a photo of Brownies sitting around a campfire (June, Girl Scouts of America, $1.00). The Girl Scout Calendar provides more than just photographs of scouts at work or play. Each month highlights important dates, both

21

for scouts and for various religions, as well as holidays. For example, October 31 is not only Halloween, but the birth date of Juliet Gordon Low, founder of the Girl Scouts of America. For budding astronomers, the calendar also provides the phases of the moon. The first page of the calendar provides a brief description of scouting. The last pages provide a view of the year's holidays at a glance, as well as an area code map. And the final page thanks you for your support.

In my little sister's room there is a fascinating drawing of a Laotian family above the month of May (my sister is always behind the times). Her calendar costs $6.00 from UNICEF. On my mother's desk this week I see a stunning photo of sunset in the Sierra Nevada Mountains, courtesy of the Sierra Club and my mother's $8.00. Dad's appointment book does not come from anywhere in particular, but for the vinyl protective cover and week-at-a-glance convenience he paid $12.50. The UNICEF calendar opens with two full pages, reproducing the 1959 United Nations Declaration of the rights of the Child, explaining the work of UNICEF, describing the calendar, and highlighting several of the world holidays found in the calendar. (The descriptions are continued on the last two pages.) The art in the calendar is produced by children from around the world, and each month features holidays from at least fifteen countries and five religions. The last page of the calendar provides a form for making contributions to the organization. The Sierra Club calendar is really a work of art. Spiral bound, with a firm cover, it looks more like a photography book than a desk calendar. The first pages include stunning photos and a description of the goals of the club, while the final pages offer an address book and a history of the Sierra club, complete with a call for membership and a list of offices and chapters of the club. On the last page is a membership form. But this calendar is to be savored for the full-page photos accompanying each week's page. Listings are confined to major holidays and phases of the moon, but the photographs of birds, animals, lakes, mountains, and plant life are breath-taking. The old insurance company calendars cannot compare with the beauty of this one.

In contrast, the week-at-a-glance calendar is rather dull to look at. But it is extremely interesting to read. The first pages include a list of the dates of major holidays in the United States and Canada for two years, as well as an area code map complete with time zones; a list of toll-free numbers for airlines, hotels, railroads, auto rental agencies, and credit card companies; a chart of weights and measures; a list of months with their birthstones; and an auto maintenance record. The final pages include a calorie counter, first aid measures, a mileage chart between major cities, and an address book. The beginning of each month features a monthly calendar along with a page designed to keep an expense account, and each week's pages include space for writing in appointments, a blank area labeled "goals for the week," and an inspirational quotation. This is the calendar to fill your every need.

And my own calendars? I must admit, they vary from year to year. Last year it was a Doonesbury desk calendar, with a cartoon for every week, and funny quotations for most days ($7.50).  This year it is a Far Side day-by-day calendar--

very simple, with a cartoon for each date, and nothing else ($6.95).  Next year I think

I will get serious with a new-word-a-day calendar.  That calendar includes a complete

dictionary definition of an obscure word for each day of the year ($7.95).  The

cartoon calendars offer few extras, but the jokes themselves keep me laughing long

after the date to which they are attached has passed.  Nor will I find much more than

dates and definitions in the word-a-day calendar, but I intend to use this one for

serious business, and I cannot afford distractions in my quest for a better vocabulary.

Of course, if I change my mind, I can choose from a large assortment of cartoon

characters, cats, dogs, horses, cars, great art, classical literature, and who knows

what else, all with price tags in the same $6.00 to $8.00 range.  It seems that

calendars are no longer designed simply to tell us the date and remind us of a local

service establishment.  Now calendars are designed to entertain, to inform, to inspire,

and to make money.


I must admit that today's calendars are far more interesting and informative than

the ones I remember from my childhood.  But somehow they do not seem so

personal.  I may know a few Girl Scouts or Sierra Club members, but UNICEF

headquarters is far away, the cartoonists live in a world very different from my small

town, and I never could establish a personal relationship with a dictionary. These new

calendars do not come from someone I know.  And they are not free anymore, either.


24

*The subject is handled very well here--most of us are familiar with all kinds of calendars, but we really don't think about how they've changed over the years. The use of parentheses is particularly effective, as is the informal tone that creates closeness between reader and writer. Organization, however, poses a problem. At times the general description of a calendar is followed immediately by the specific analysis of everything i the calendar offers, and at times the two descriptions are separated. Consider the purpose of the paper: what point is being made about current calendars? With purpose in mind, rearrange the material.*

**Exercise 3:**    The Informative Essay--Revising for Audience Awareness
                  (*S & S* Handbook Chapter 1c)

**Focusing on the end comment and the underlined sections, revise the
following draft by including the details and explanations necessary for
a general audience. (Additional details are provided after the end
comment.)**

### The New Water Sports

There was a time when water sports consisted of swimming and boating. The

most unusual sight on the water might be a sailboat with brightly colored sails or a

cabin cruiser with a collection of flags. Then came waterskis and surfboards.

Powerboats carried in their wake tiny figures in orange lifejackets, many of whom

ended up being dunked in chilly waters after a missed turn. Huge waves sported

splashes of red and blue as daring creatures balanced on what looked like fancy

ironing boards surrounded by white foam. It seemed for a while that people had

everything they needed to enjoy themselves on lakes and rivers, as well as in the

ocean. But things have changed. Today visitors to various shores will see some

strange sights out there on the water.

At the seashore, for example, bathers might see bodyboarders vying with surfers

for the best waves. The two look almost alike while they paddle out to the surf, but

bodyboarders will be wearing flippers. (A surfer cannot wear flippers.) The sports

are somewhat similar in that they both involve using a board to ride powerful waves,

but the boards are not used in the same way. A body board is about half the length of a surfboard, lighter, and contoured to fit the body. Body boards are much less expensive than surfboards, and easier to carry around. They are also less likely to get away from the bodyboarder, because of the leash. Bodyboarders claim that their sport is as much fun as surfing, but safer and easier to learn. They may be right, because the sport has enjoyed steadily increasing popularity in the last several years.

In addition to surfing and bodyboarding, sailboarding has become a popular ocean sport. Sailboarders ride standing up, hanging on to the bar. In very rough waters, or for certain competitions, sailboarders will attach themselves to the bar. The sail is manipulated in much the same way as the sail on a boat. Sailboarders present an especially beautiful sight on a clear, sunny day, as the multicolored sails stand out against the blue of the ocean and sky. But they also provide a good illustration of frustration when an unfortunate sailboarder tries again and again to right the sail, only to fly along a few feet before tipping over once again. Sailboarders, however, insist that the sport can be learned quickly and easily.

On lakes and rivers, the most unusual sight you will see will probably look like someone with unusually large feet walking across the water. Skijaking is a very new sport. Skyjakers fit their feet into the boots, and use a paddle to help themselves along. In fact, watching a skyjaker move on the water is similar to watching a canoer. But the skills involved have more to do with downhill skiiing than canoeing. Like skiing, skijaking involves shifting the body's weight; and like skis, skijaks are equipped with bindings that will release in case of a fall. Skyjakers are often seen making their way down a river or across a lake in groups, providing onlookers with a sight that is sometimes awe-inspiring, and sometimes amusing. While not as popular as bodyboarding or sailboarding, skijaking promises to gain more and more followers in the future.

Once the prospect of a vacation on the water was a relaxing one. Travelers might enjoy lying on the sand with a good book, taking a leisurely swim, or perhaps going for a brisk sail. Now the options have expanded. It is hard to concentrate on a book with so much activity going on in the water. And it is even harder to decide which of the many possible water sports to try. For those who have trouble making up their minds, it may be far less demanding simply to forget the vacation altogether and return to work early.

*Both the introduction and conclusion of this essay are strong; they involve the reader and present the writer as informed and pleasant. Organization is also clear and logical. What poses a problem, however, is the information itself. How much can a general audience be expected to know about skiing, for example? And what does a boot that releases mean? Look at the underlined sections, and ask the questions that an uninformed reader might ask. Then provide the necessary details and explanations.*

# DETAILS

BODYBOARDING: Riders use flippers to help them move out to the waves more quickly--they can do this because they don't need to use their toes to balance on the board the way surfers do. Lay almost flat on the board, but sometimes, like surfers, they balance in half-kneeling position. Board contoured to fit the body, shorter/lighter than surfboards, and less expensive/easier to carry.

SAILBOARDING: Take a sail from a sailboat, attach it to a bodyboard, and you have a sailboard. (Real sailboards are designed proportionately.) Bar surrounds sail near board, rider holds on to bar for balance, and sometimes uses flexible belt to attach him/herself to bar--rough waters, competition.

SKYJAKING: Comes from skiiing and kayaking. Kayak a canoe that has a hole in the top only big enough for the one canoer. Skyjakers use double-bladed canoe-like paddles to move along, but move body from side to side for balance like in skiing. Boots are eleven feet long, and have releases like skis. Boot releases from the foot in a fall so rider won't be injured severely.

**Exercise 4: The Analytical Essay--Revising for Coherence**
**(*S & S* Handbook Chapter 4d)**

Focusing on the end comment and the underlined sections, revise the
following draft by incorporating techniques of coherence (transitional
expressions, pronouns, parallel structures). (Note that the names of
television programs are underlined to represent italics, not to indicate
problem areas.)


The Dick Van Dyke Show: An Analysis


A look at reruns of situation comedies of the 1950s and 60s reveals a single mold,
and from this mold a number of programs were cut, with very few variations. Leave
It To Beaver, Father Knows Best, The Donna Reed Show, The Adventures of Ozzie
and Harriet, Dennis the Menace--all of these programs featured what was supposed to
be the typical American family. These all-white, middle-class, Protestant, suburban
families were headed by a strong father who was the sole support of his family, and a
complacent mother who found fulfillment in deferring to the needs of her husband,
children, and home nurtured the family. The children (most of them boys) got into
the usual minor trouble expected of children, but guided by their mothers' love and
their fathers' wisdom, they never strayed very far from the straight and narrow path.


One of the most popular was The Dick Van Dyke Show, with Van Dyke playing
comedy writer Rob Petrie, and Mary Tyler Moore playing his wife, Laura. The
couple had the required house in the suburbs and a son, Richie. The Dick Van Dyke
Show fit the sitcom mold quite nicely: Rob went off to work in the city each day,

leaving Laura to care for Richie and the house, and to plan the various social functions Rob and Laura hosted at their home. Laura dutifully cooked and cleaned. She was always fussing about her appearance, and she meddled in her husband's business affairs, and was generally playing the typical wife. Richie, raised with such strong family values, got into a little mischief now and then, but always repented. The Petrie's neighbors, Jerry the dentist and Millie, his wife, were a little silly (a character device necessary to show how solid the Petries were), but like the Petries, they lived a life of contentment in postwar America. Rob and Laura and Jerry and Millie never encountered poverty, never discovered that a friend was abusing his children, never dealt with the breakup of a marriage. Living in America meant living without concerns--it was a paradise on earth.

Of course something would occasionally threaten the peaceful existence of the Petries and their friends. In one episode Laura felt the pangs of a lost career when she was asked to fill in for an ailing dancer on the Allen Brady Show (for which her husband Rob was the head comedy writer). After two weeks of full-time work, however, she realized, as did her family, that everyone is unhappy when a wife and mother returns to work. The TV sitcom family could not survive a working mother. Once Rob became convinced that his friend and coworker Buddy was seeing another woman. But it turned out that she was the wife of Buddy's rabbi, who was preparing Buddy for his Bar Mitzvah, an honor denied him when he was young because of his family's poverty. Through a plot, not only did the program reinforce the notion of the indestructable marriage, but it also reminded us that Buddy had lived the American Dream by working hard and making a success of himself.

One feature of The Dick Van Dyke Show deserves a good deal of credit. Buddy was probably the only character on television in those days who was not assumed to be a member of a mainstream Protestant church. This fact in itself was a significant accomplishment for the program. And the respect and reverence accorded Jewish tradition in this episode was something rarely found on television at the time.

The Dick Van Dyke Show was a ground breaker in the area of women's rights. Certainly the portrayal of Laura as insatiably curious, overconcerned about her appearance, and prone to fits of hysterics was stereotypical and not very flattering to women, but the show also featured as one of Rob's cowriters a young, talented, attractive, single woman. Sally hatched frequent plots to find herself a husband. Her character was primarily represented as a female operating competently and equally in an all-male atmosphere: the star of the fictional program, the producer, and the other two writers were all men, and with them Sally held her own. They even feared that she had outgrown them in one episode when she became the darling of a television talk-show host. She returned to her job not because she could not make it on her own, but because she loved her work.

In the area of race relations The Dick Van Dyke Show was a groundbreaker. One episode, a flashback to the birth of little Richie, featured a comically distraught Rob convinced that the hospital had switched babies, and the one in their bassinet really belonged to another couple. His telephone conversation with the other father revealed that he thought the whole situation amusing, and when they turned up at the Petrie's door, the reason for his amusement was clear: the family was black. To confront a racial issue in such a way was unheard of in the early sixties, and The Dick Van Dyke Show did it more than once. One epidose featured a harried Rob and Laura desperately trying to hide their dye-blackened hands (the result of an accident involving a homemade costume for Richie) at an awards dinner for a civil rights group. The Petries, after many humorous attempts to explain the gloves, finally removed them sheepishly, realizing that their hosts were understanding human beings who would be able to appreciate the irony of the situation, and laugh with them at their needless concern. The Petries learned a lesson about race relations in the episode. And an audience unaccustomed to such lessons learned about race relations.

The Dick Van Dyke Show may well have reinforced some of the unpleasant stereotypes of the late fifties and early sixties, clinging to a vision of America that simply was not accurate. It reached out on occasion, and it did bring a few of the issues that would soon become prominent into the living rooms of America long before those issues became big news. For whatever the reason, the people involved with that program recognized their responsibility to a changing country.

*The analysis of the program is quite sharp: the paper focuses on key issues that distinguish between programs that play it safe and those that take risks. Examples are also clearly presented. What would make the paper stronger is closer attention to coherence--appropriate use of pronouns, parallel structures, and transitional expressions would pull the ideas together. Sections that need attention are underlined.*

**Exercise 5: The Persuasive Essay--Revising for Support**
**(*S & S* Handbook Chapter 6d)**

Focusing on the end comment and the underlined sections, revise the
following draft by providing supporting evidence and explanation for
general statements. (Supporting information is provided after the end
comment.)

Just Say No to U.S.ENGLISH

While most people in the United States speak English as their first language, and

most public business is conducted in English, this country has no "official" language.

Thus it is possible for public schools to offer non-English speaking children academic

instruction in their own language, and for the government to print ballots and other

official documents in more than one language. Bilingual education, ballots, and

government communication is becoming more common in areas where immigrants

have kept their own language.

Some people consider this situation to be a problem. To solve that problem, in

1983 former Senator S. I. Hayakawa formed an organization called U.S.ENGLISH

(USE), with the intent of abolishing bilingual education, eliminating bilingual public

communication, and passing a constitutional amendment to make English the official

language of the United States. Hayakawa's solution has enjoyed considerable

support: thirteen states have already passed legislation consistent with his goals, and

ten more are considering such legislation. Supporters of these bills claim that they

will stop the decline in English skills, force immigrants to learn the language, and

37

community, but we may also discover that a nation built on many cultures does not need one "official" language.

*Organization of argument is clear and logical, as are reasons for position . Opponent's position is stated clearly early in paper, preparing reader for response. Underlined sections, however, need support. Readers have to be able to understand where this position comes from and why it is reasonable.*

## SUPPORTING INFORMATION

OFFICIAL LANGUAGE:   USE legislation doesn't provide funds for teaching English to adult immigrants.  How can we insist upon English as our official language if we don't teach it to them?

SKILLS PROBLEM: Skills problem  in all areas of the country, many English-speaking. Decline in English skills a native speakers' problem, not a second language problem.

BAN ON BILINGUAL COMMUNICATION: Public health agencies and courts can't provide translation.  Mother brings child to health clinic and doesn't speak language--defendant being tried in language he/she can't understand.  Voters can't read English ballots.

WHOSE PROBLEM IS IT?  Haven for the underprivileged--that's what  the US is supposed to be--this  legislation that discriminates against those underprivileged immigrants.  They have the problem, not us--so solutions should be designed to help them, not us.

WHAT WE MUST DO: More classes--waiting lists very long in LA, NY;  translation services-- their needs must be met, their rights protected until they learn English.

**Exercise 6:    The Research Paper--Revising for Proper Use of Sources**
**(*S & S* Handbook Chapters 31, 33)**

**Use the student's notes in the text to document sources properly,**
**present quotations and paraphrases accurately, and prepare the Works**
**Cited page.**


Insomnia:  The Waking Nightmare


Little children hate to do it, teenagers do it until noon, and adults never seem to

get enough of it.  "It" is sleep.  We all need a certain amount of sleep, but such a

simple need can often cause great problems in our lives.  Some people, for example,

suffer from narcolepsy, a disease which results in one's falling asleep at any time in

any position.  Others have the opposite problem-- insomnia, or the inability to fall

asleep.  Because it is a disease, narcolepsy requires medical care, often including

medication.  Insomnia, on the other hand, is not a disease.  It can result from a

number of different causes, and thus each case requires a good deal of study before it

can be treated.

> *Insert quote from  p. 43 of Hopson's article : "Insomnia is a*
>
> *symptom, like chest pain or headache (leave out rest of sentence).*
>
> *And successful treatment depends on understanding and addressing*
>
> *each patient's special mix of contributing causes, from biological*
>
> *tendencies to medical and emotional factors, to plain bad habits."*

During the past twenty years, medical researchers have spent  considerable time and

money studying insomnia, not only because the condition is so complex, but also because it is "the most commonly experienced sleep disorder." *(from p. 174 of Hobson book)*

Insomnia has several forms, some of which are little more than annoyances. Many people, for example, have experienced "'transient' insomnia--the *(leave out part of quotation)* usually not-too-serious kind that lasts no more than a few nights and is triggered by jet lag, a fight with the boss, an upcoming test or some other schedule disruption or stress." *(quoted from p. 44 of Hopson article )* Travel is one of the more frequent causes of transient insomnia. The person whose job requires travel to different time zones often finds him or herself unable to get to sleep at a reasonable hour. Expert Dianne Hales advises travelers on short trips (one to three days) to continue using home time as much as possible, even if that means going to bed at 8:00 p.m. and rising at 4:00 a.m.. On long trips, travelers are advised to begin operating in the new time zone immediately, no matter how difficult the first day may be. If possible, they should try to arrive at their destination late so that they can go to bed immediately. They are also encouraged to rise at the appropriate time on the first day of the trip, regardless of whether or not it is necessary to their schedule. The body can adjust to a new time zone very quickly, but only if its owner insists. *(material comes from Maggio's one-page article, but it's Hale's idea)*

Unfortunately, only a fraction of insomniacs fall into the transient category. Far more suffer from short-term insomnia (sleeplessness that lasts from several days to several weeks at a time). *(paraphrased from Hopson's article, p. 44. Documentation same as for quotation?)* Frequently such cases result from stress on the job or problems in the family, and far too often, such people resort to sleeping pills. Sleep-inducing drugs, however, are as dangerous as they are popular. Most experts agree that the more a person uses drugs to get to sleep, the more likely it is that he or she will become dependent on the drugs and be unable to get to sleep naturally. The same phenomenon occurs when insomniacs resort to taking alcohol in order to get to sleep. In both cases, the body comes to rely on the drug to induce sleep. Once the person stops taking the sleeping pills or the alcohol, the insomnia returns. Researchers call this phenomenon "rebound insomnia." *(This is Hopson's term, from p.48. Not sure if she made it up. What's the most responsible way to document it?)* Sleeping pills often trap the sufferer in a frustrating cycle of insomnia, followed by drug-induced sleep, followed by rebound insomnia. Drug dependence is often the result of such treatment.

What should the sleepless sufferer do? Those who suffer from transient or short-term insomnia can often be helped. One of the most important discoveries that researchers have made is that insomnia can be treated at home, without drugs, and with very little medical knowledge on the patient's part. If the cause of the insomnia is job or family stress, doctors often advise that the right attitude can bring on sleep.

If you were to find yourself suffering from stress-related insomnia, doctors might prescribe a relatively simple set of steps to induce sleep. Such home treatments often involve making lists of pressing problems and the steps you will take to work on those problems the following day. This practice should produce a sense of control, of tackling difficulties head-on. *(All of this comes from the Moskowitz article, pages 121 and 122.)* Once you are in bed, you should try to relax your mind as well as your body. According to J. Allan Hobson, it is possible to push stressful thoughts out of your mind: "By an act of conscious will, we may substitute neutral, even nonmeaningful thoughts (like the word <u>one</u>, or <u>omm</u>) for our preoccupations. To aid in this process, we may visualize a pleasant scene (like the mountains or the ocean). As we meditate, *(substitute the words "we give ourselves" for what the author wrote)* a chance to quiet down." *(page 181. Long quotations treated the same as short ones?)* The one thing you should avoid thinking about at all costs is trying to fall asleep.

> *Insert Carl Sherman's <u>Working Woman</u> page 194 quotation:*
> *"Ironically, one worry that's almost guaranteed to banish sleep is the fear of sleeplessness itself."*

These bedtime activities should help you drift off into peaceful sleep.


While the bedtime ritual is important, treatment of short-term insomnia involves more. Perhaps the most crucial part of the treatment is the routine. Insomniacs are advised to set a specific schedule for retiring and rising, and to stick to the schedule. Thus if you are unable to nod off until 3:00 a.m., you still must rise at the normal

7:00 a.m. (or whatever time is normal) rather than "sleeping in." The routine will help the body become accustomed to a particular sleep pattern. Conversely, if you find that you are unable to get to sleep at your normal bedtime, experts agree that you should not stay in bed.

> *Insert Moskowitz's advice to business executives: "get up and do*
> *something useful that doesn't take much concentration--straightening a*
> *few dresser drawers, perhaps, or sorting out which suits need pressing*
> *or cleaning." (page 121)*

Some doctors suggest old fashioned cures such as a hot bath before bed. The temperature changes caused by the bath ease the patient's tension and stress, and prepare the body for sleep. *(paraphrased from the Welles article, page 6)* Exercise during the day (not right before sleep) is also recommended, as is avoidance of alcohol and caffeine. And avoiding caffeine does not simply mean to switch to decaffeinated coffee. In addition to coffee, foods that contain caffeine include tea, cola drinks, and chocolate. Finally, you should ask your doctor or pharmacist about any medication you may be taking. Among drugs that can interfere with sleep are some used to treat thyroid and heart problems, certain birth control pills, and several antidepressants. *(paraphrased from the Hopson article, page 45)* Careful adherence to these steps usually result in success for the short-term insomniac.

The worst type of insomnia cannot be treated so simply. Chronic insomnia can last for years, and researchers are still trying to determine its causes and treatments.

45

Some studies have revealed a possible biological factor in chronic insomnia. Researchers at Dartmouth Medical School's Sleep Disorders Clinic describe the condition this way: "*(material at the beginning of the quotation left out)* sleep and wakefulness are probably governed by two brain systems: an arousal system and a sleep (or "hypnagogic") system. Since arousal can override sleep, if sleep is to occur, the arousal system must subside and allow the hypnagogic system to take over. Insomniacs *(some material left out)* may have a chronically overactive arousal system or a chronically underactive hypnagogic system." *(long quotation from page 44 of the Hopson article. Treat the same way as short quotation?)* Treatment of such cases is exhausting, for both doctor and patient alike. Diagnosis alone often involves personal interviews, psychological tests, medical histories, physical examinations, and monitored nights in a sleep laboratory. Once diagnosed, patients may be treated through counseling, psychotherapy, training in relaxation techniques, medication, and biofeedback. The treatment depends upon the diagnosis, so each case is treated differently. *(paraphrased from pages 48 and 49 of Hopson's article)* Needless to say, the road to peaceful sleep for the chronic insomniac is a long and expensive one.

Those of us who have no problem getting to sleep have no idea of how difficult the world of the insomniac can be. Insomnia, whether transient, short-term, or chronic, whether caused by stress, travel, or physical problems, condemns the sufferer to frustration, fatigue, and ill-temper. Without help, the chronic insomniac can develop other health problems, not to mention psychological disorders.

Fortunately, researchers are continually discovering new aids for the poor soul who spends the night tossing, turning, groaning, pacing--anything but sleeping.

References used:

J., Allan Hobson's book called Sleep, published by Scientific American Library in New York in 1989.

Daniel B. Moskowitz's article called Saying Good Night to Your Insomnia , in the January 27, 1986 issue of the weekly magazine Business Week, pages 121 and 122.

Janet L. Hopson's article called The Unraveling of Insomnia in the June 1988 issue of Psychology Today magazine, pages 43 through 49.

Carl Sherman's article called The Truth about a Good Night's Sleep, in the November 1988 issue of Working Woman magazine, starting on page 194 and finishing later in the magazine.

Christine Maggio's one-page article called How to Beat Jet Lag in the April 21-23 1989 issue of the weekly magazine USA Weekend, page 6.

Gloria Welles' half-page article called Losing Sleep Over Weekends, on the same page as Christine Maggio's article.

## PART III

REVISING PARAGRAPHS:
CORRECT AND EFFECTIVE SENTENCES
(*S & S* Handbook Chapters 13, 14, 16-19)

The content of the paragraphs in this section is interesting, but all of
the paragraphs need revising.  In some paragraphs actual errors in
punctuation and sentence structure need correction; in others the
editing will involve making stylistic choices.  Revise each paragraph
according to the instructions, first making appropriate corrections
and/or stylistic changes in the paragraph itself, and then copying the
edited paragraph on a separate sheet of paper.  (In cases of stylistic
choices, do not worry about finding the one "correct" revision.  There
may be several possible revisions from which to choose.)

Exercise 1:    Revising to Eliminate Sentence Fragments
               (*S & S* Handbook Chapter 13)

Incomplete sentences, or fragments, can make a passage very difficult
to read.  In the following paragraph, fragments not only make the
sentences sound choppy, but they also force the reader to go back in
order to understand several sentences.  Correct the fragments in the
paragraph, either by joining them to other sentences, or by making
them complete sentences.

On April 17, 1906, at 5:15 AM. The city felt the first tremor.  By Thursday

morning at the same time, virtually the entire city was either burned out.  Or in

flames.  The Great San Fransisco Earthquake remains one of the most terrifying

moments in our country's history.  The city had been a monument to

twentieth-century technology.  The skyline dotted with skyscrapers, the lavish homes

serviced by gas and electricity, and the economy  booming.  But in twenty-four hours

it was all gone.  It is interesting.  That the quake itself accounted for only a part of the

damage.  With water and gas lines broken, the fires that raged throughout the city

following the earthquake destroyed everything.  That remained standing.  Journalist

and author Jack London watched as walls of flame not only moved steadily

throughout the city.  But created winds that spread the fire.  The quake, one of the

greatest disasters the country had ever suffered.

When independent clauses are joined incorrectly, the result can be
confusing or distracting to the reader. Often a comma splice or a
fused sentences forces the reader to reread sentences several times in
order to figure out what they mean. The following paragraph suffers
from several errors. Revise the paragraph, correcting the comma
splices and fused sentences.

People who climb the rugged mountains of northwestern United States and
Canada are highly skilled and extremely courageous, performing feats that most of us
would never dare attempt. Waiting for them on the highest peaks, however, are
ordinary-looking animals who move easily from rock to rock, they climb in areas that
are impossible for humans to reach. These creatures, they make adventurers look like
amateurs, are mountain goats. What does the mountain goat have that even the best
climbers do not have? Plenty! In the first place, the goats' legs are very short,
keeping their bodies close to the ground and improving their balance, at the end of
those legs are hooves made of leather-like pads surrounded by firm, hard edges. The
pads keep the goats from slipping, the edges help them dig into ice and snow. Travel
is not the only use for these hooves, however, they also come in handy when the
goats get hungry. It is not easy to find plants to eat when there is a ten-inch
snowcover. Human hands are no match for the mountain goat's hooves nor are
human-made clothes a match for the mountain goat's coat. Two layers of hair, one of
them has hollow strands that hold heat, protect the animal in temperatures as low as
-50°. The protection and the ability that nature provides free for the mountain goat
would cost a human being hundreds of dollars and months of training. And even

**Exercise 3:    Revising for Conciseness** (*S & S* Handbook Chapter 16)

**Unnecessary and repetitive words and phrases can interfere with the reader's enjoyment (and sometimes understanding) of a paragraph. The stylistic effect of this passage is one of considerable clutter. Edit by eliminating the excess.**


To people accustomed to seeing their President on television almost each and every day, one of the great wonders of Franklin Delano Roosevelt's presidency must seem to be of the utmost insignificance. And yet to Americans who lived during the time of the 1930's, hearing their President conduct his "Fireside Chats" on the radio was indeed wonderful. Regardless of his other accomplishments, which included such various achievements in many fields such as steering the country through a great depression and a great war, Roosevelt will always and forever be remembered as the first president to come into the homes of most Americans. It was the technology that allowed the Chief Executive to speak to his fellow citizens that was, of course, primarily responsible for the transformation of the Presidency, but in point of fact, Roosevelt's style made that transformation a smooth one. Unlike many of his predecessors who held the office before he did, Roosevelt was casual, even informal, in his speeches. This informality endeared him to a nation that found itself in the most desperate need of a leader in whom they could place their trust. Roosevelt, at least in his chats with the public, did not disappoint them.

**Exercise 4:   Revising for Coordination and Subordination**
              (*S & S* Handbook Chapter 17)

Proper use of coordination and subordination helps the reader see
relationships between ideas in a paragraph.  In the following
paragraph, coordination and subordination are sometimes improperly
used, sometimes missing, and sometimes overused.  Revise the
paragraph, using coordination and subordination effectively.


The Walt Disney Studio is generally credited with introducing sophisticated

animation to film.  Cartoons featuring Mickey Mouse and friends first appeared in the

1930s.  These characters have been entertaining audiences for several generations.

During the last fifteen years, however, another era for animation has begun in

Portland, Oregon.  That is where Will Vinton has perfected a revolutionary form of

animation.  Vinton's process involves giving life, or animating, figures made from

clay and plastic, and it is called Claymation.  The process is a difficult one.  The

figures are ready for filming, and animators must adjust them for each frame of the

film, making sure that facial expressions and positions are exactly as the director

wants them.  Sometimes it can take over two months to prepare a minute of film, so

when a film is completed,  the effect is usually well worth the effort, because the

characters indeed appear to be alive, far more alive than in traditional animation, and

now Mickey and his friends have some tough competition.

**Exercise 5:    Revising for Parallelism  (*S & S* Handbook Chapter 18)**

**Parallel words and parallel structures help a writer express similar ideas or information.  The following paragraph is less effective than it might be because of failure to use parallel forms in appropriate places. Revise the paragraph, using parallel words and structures where they are called for.**

I have often heard my grandparents refer to taking a "Cook's Tour" when they take a short trip, or if someone from a distance visits us. I often wondered where the term came from, so I decided to look it up. Imagine my surprise when I discovered that the term actually refers to brief tours conducted by Mr. Thomas Cook of Great Britain in the mid-eighteen-hundreds. Before this time, travel had been a luxury reserved for the rich, the class of people who have plenty of leisure, and educated people. But Cook brought travel to the masses. His tours were open to carpenters, clerks, nurses, and also allowed to use the tours were shopkeepers. For a reasonable price, a middle-class traveler could book a complete package with Cook without worrying about any of the arrangements normally associated with a trip. Cook took care of buying railroad tickets, he made hotel reservations, arrangements for meals were made by him, and securing entrance to museums and tourist attractions. His employees even provided medical advice! As might be expected, many among the upper classes considered Cook's tours highly objectionable. They were accustomed to having the attractions of Europe to themselves, and did not appreciate the sight of fifty middle-class Englishmen and women being led through the ruins of ancient Rome by a professional guide. But their protests went unheard; nobody notices their discomfort. Democracy had finally arrived in the travel industry.

Exercise 6:    Revising for Variety and Emphasis
                (*S & S* Handbook Chapter 19)

Sometimes a passage seems correct as far as grammar, punctuation and
sentence structure are concerned, but it still needs editing. When
many of the sentences in a paragraph are of similar length and
structure, the stylistic effect is closer to that of a list than a smoothly
written paragraph. Vary the sentence length and structure in the
following paragraph so that it reads more smoothly.

Workers building the pyramids of Giza in Egypt seven centuries before the birth
of Jesus discovered a massive statue that has intrigued the world ever since. The
Sphinx depicted a creature with the head of a man and the body of a reclining lion. It
has endured for almost three thousand years, but not without problems. People
carved graffiti on the Sphinx's toe in the second century AD. A religious fanatic tried
to destroy the statue in the sixteenth century. He succeeded only in removing its
nose. A British colonel in the nineteenth century tried to determine whether or not
the Sphinx was hollow by drilling holes into it. Thirty centuries of weather have
taken their toll on the statue. Scientists now are finally trying to make sure that the
Sphinx survives. They are using thermal photography to see where there are pockets
of heat in the statue. They are hoping to find areas of dampness that might erode the
stone. Human beings were once the greatest enemies of the Sphinx. They are now
using their knowledge to preserve one of the great wonders of the world.

**Exercise 7:**    **Revising for Correct and Effective Sentences
(Summary Exercise)**

**The following paragraph needs to be revised for a number of
problems, all of which have been covered in exercises 1 through 6.
Revise carefully.**

The early history of our country is frequently told through tales of the men who
explored new territories and established settlements in the wilderness. Their stories
are fascinating, and they are not the only tales of colonial times and westward
expansion. Equally interesting are the stories of the women who transformed rough
houses into homes and made communities out of scattered settlements. Because of
the harshness of New England winters and the isolation the western frontier, the life
of colonial and pioneer women was both difficult and lonely. One of the ways in
which these women fulfilled their need for companionship was through quilting bees.
Quilts were valuable to the settlers, and they provided needed warmth during cold
winter nights. They also allowed women to make use of scraps of cloth. The cloth
was left over from making clothing for the family. The quilting bee took place when
many women would come together for periods ranging from several hours to an entire
day. The women found the quilting bee to be a way to work while socializing. Many
times, quilting bees were held for a specific occasion, often a birth or a wedding.
Because there was little money for families to spend on individual presents, and even
less time for each woman to make a unique gift, women in a community would gather
and make a quilt for the new baby or bride. As the country grew and prospered,
however, the art of quilting and the practice of quilting bees largely disappeared

women no longer needed to make use of every scrap of cloth, and other forms of socialization made quilting bees unnecessary. It was not until the country's Bicentennial in 1976 that quilting began to enjoy a revival. By focusing our attention on our cultural heritage. That celebration reintroduced us to a part of our past. Today quilting bees are organized by women (and some men) who need a break not from isolation so much as from the stresses of modern life, many of today's quilters say that their pastime makes them feel closer to the women who helped found this country.

## PART IV

EDITING PARAGRAPHS:
GRAMMAR AND WORD CHOICE
(*S & S* Handbook Chapters 8-11, 21)

The content of the paragraphs in this section is interesting, but all of
the paragraphs need editing for correct grammar and word choice. Edit
each paragraph according to the instructions, first making appropriate
corrections in the paragraphs themselves, and then copying the edited
paragraph on a separate sheet of paper.

Exercise 8:    Editing for Correct Use of Verbs
              (*S & S* Handbook Chapter 8)

**The following passage contains a number of verb errors, making the paragraph difficult to follow. Correct any errors in tense and tense sequence, and rephrase any inappropriate use of passive voice.**


Most of us consider that when we are electing a new President, we are making a choice that will remain with us for four years. If our choice has been found to be satisfactory, we may decide to have another four years of that person's policies. No president may serve for more than two consecutive terms of office, thereby to prevent someone from becoming too influential in our country's government. But most presidents have been able to make their policies live on after them--at least in the federal courts. One of the President's duties are to appoint federal judges, who serve on the bench not for the term of the President's office, but for life. One of the most significant appointments a president can make is that of Supreme Court Justice. To appoint someone to the highest court of the land is a very important privilege, and some presidents are more influential than others. While Ronald Reagan was in office, for example, he has appointed four Supreme Court Justices. This takes on added significance when you consider that the Supreme Court consist of only nine justices. Since Reagan's appointees are all in their fifties or early sixties, we can expect that they will have served on the Court for a long time to come. Thus one president, even though he or she serves for only four or eight years, could influence policy for decades to come.

**Exercise 9:     Editing for Correct Pronoun Reference and Case**
**(*S & S* Handbook Chapters 9, 10)**

**The following paragraph contains a number of problems in pronoun reference and case. Reference poses a particular problem because both subjects of the paragraph are male, and both are poets, making the use of the masculine singular personal pronoun confusing for the reader. Locate and correct the pronoun errors in the selection. (Occasionally correcting one pronoun will eliminate the need to correct a subsequent pronoun.)**

While he was still unknown, the poet Langston Hughes worked for a time as a busboy in a Washington hotel restaurant. One evening he discovered that the poet Vachel Lindsay, who Hughes respected greatly, was dining there before going to a poetry reading of his works. This prompted the busboy to gather up all his courage and place several of his poems on Lindsay's table, pausing only long enough to tell him what they were and that he liked his work. Knowing that him speaking on behalf of another poet would be helpful, the famous poet read some of his poems at the reading, and announced to the newspapers that he had discovered a new Black poet. The next day, newspaper reporters and photographers greeted Hughes as he arrived at the hotel, photographing him in his busboy's uniform. They would recognize his name from this point on.

**Exercise 10:  Editing for Agreement (*S & S* Handbook Chapter 11)**

**The following passage contains a number of errors in agreement.
Correct the errors in noun-verb agreement, and those in
pronoun-antecedent agreement.**

During the past century, once-deadly diseases like smallpox has become treatable

because of medical discoveries.  Smallpox, along with polio, have been all but

eliminated by vaccines.  In addition, antibiotics successfully battle infections, and

decongestants ease the symptoms of the common cold.  While some diseases remain

untreatable or incurable, most is now under the control of medical technology.

Recently, however, medical researchers have rediscovered the healing powers of

good nutrition.  Almost everyone remembers their grandmother's old cure for many

illnesses, chicken soup.  Now it seems that our grandmothers may have been medical

pioneers.  To put it simply, sometimes the right food is the best medicine.  Oat bran is

one of those foods that keeps us healthy.  It is as effective as prescribed drugs in

maintaining desirable cholesterol levels.  If you consider that the appropriate cereals,

muffins and bread costs about 85% less than the prescription medicines designed to

control cholesterol, this is good news indeed.  Other foods have medicinal value as

well, including spinach and broccoli, which lower cancer risk; cabbage and milk,

which help prevent ulcers;  and yogurt, which singlehandedly lowers cholesterol

levels, improves the immune system, and improves bowel functions.  While the

medical community still are not sure of why some foods act as they do, some

researchers are becoming increasingly certain that old "home cures" have survived

from generation to generation for a very good reason:  it works.

**Exercise 11: Editing for Appropriate Diction**
*(S & S Handbook Chapter 21)*

**In the following paragraph, shifts between formal diction and slang, as well as inappropriate use of technical language, create a confusing tone. Substitute appropriate, informal usage for the slang and the formal and technical language.**

If you have had the opportunity to listen to a phonograph record from roughly threescore years ago, you will recall the scratchy, tinny sound of the songs you heard. The records themselves look strange today as well: played at 78 rotations per minute (as opposed to 33 for most recordings today), the records were thick and of considerable weight compared to the thin, lightweight vinyl records made since the 1950s. The 1960s saw another change in recording technology, with all the hype about cassette tapes. Cassettes were far more fragile than vinyl records, and did not enjoy as extended a duration, but they were certainly more easily conveyed by hand. In fact, the introduction of cassettes helped transform car radios into stereo entertainment systems. Regardless of the popularity of cassettes, however, serious music collectors stuck to albums--that is, until the 1980s, the decade of the CD revolution. Compact discs are the result of mind-blowing new technology, allowing discs small enough to fit into your hand to produce sound of a higher quality than anything ever produced by vinyl records. Made of molded plastic and reflective aluminum, CDs are played when a light beam from a low intensity laser is reflected and scattered alternately and read by an optical sensor, converting varying intensities of light into digital signal and thus into sound impulses. CDs are as portable as cassettes, and, since there is no contact between needle and record surface, they don't get wiped out like records do. Nor is sound messed up by small scratches or dust on the disc. Music lovers have welcomed CDs warmly as the answer to their dreams. But the dream comes with a price. No longer will we be enthralled by the art of the album cover. Reduced to the size of a compact disc cover, the finely detailed depiction of Sgt. Pepper's Lonely Hearts Club Band loses most of its magic.

**Exercise 12:** Editing for Grammar and
Word Choice (Summary Exercise)

**The following paragraph needs editing for a number of problems, all of which have been covered in exercises 8 through 11. Edit carefully.**

In the early 1920s dance in America was very traditional. At the Metropolitan Opera Ballet School in the Big Apple, students learned precise but standard techniques of dance. One student who decided that she had wanted to break away from tradition was Helen Tamiris, whom later became one of the most successful dancers, choreographers, and teachers in the field. Tamiris spent some time at the Isadora Duncan School, named for the famous innovator in modern dance technique. But she was not one of those dancers who was content to imitate others. She wanted to go beyond the personal expressiveness and lyricism of the Duncan technique, so in 1930 she split to found her own school. Her style of dance did not depend on any particular technique; rather, technique was varied by her according to the dance being performed. Negro spirituals, protest themes, and modern jazz found its way into many of her dances. One dance in particular, <u>How Long Brethren</u>, focused on black unemployment in the South and was being performed to black protest songs. This, however, did not prevent her from choreographing many musical plays, among them <u>Annie Get Your Gun</u> in 1946. Regardless of whether she was choreographing for Broadway, performing her own concerts, or imparting education to young dancers, Helen Tamiris remained a powerful force in American dance. If she would not have broken away from traditional forms, American dance would not be what it is today.

## PART V

EDITING PARAGRAPHS:
          PUNCTUATION, SPELLING, HYPHENATION
          (*S & S* Handbook Chapters 3, 22, 24-30)

The content of the paragraphs in this section is interesting, but each of
the paragraphs needs editing for one of the following:  correct
punctuation, spelling, or hyphenation.  Edit each paragraph according
to the instructions, first making appropriate corrections in the
paragraph itself, and then copying the edited paragraph in the space
provided.

**Exercise 13:  Editing for Correct Use of Commas**
**(*S & S* Handbook Chapter 24)**

**The following passage contains a number of errors in comma use:
sometimes necessary commas are left out, and sometimes unnecessary
commas are included.  Correct these errors, being careful to leave
correct sentences as they are.**


On January 6, 1839 Louis-Jacques-Mande Daguerre announced in Paris that he

had finally perfected photography.  But William Henry Fox Talbot an Englishman had

been experimenting with the photographic process, since 1835.  Talbot had coated

paper with both a salt and a silver nitrate solution and produced images of objects on

the paper after exposing them to light.  Daguerre's process was not only different, but

more complicated as well.  It involved using silver-coated copper plate in a camera

and exposing it to light.  The exposed plate was then heated, over mercury, and

bathed in a salt solution.  When Daguerre announced his results, Talbot went public

as well.  He had come up with the right combination first but Daguerre's results were

more impressive.  A sort of war began after Daguerre announced his accomplishment,

with Talbot and Daguerre vying for world attention.  Talbot's process would

eventually be the basis for modern photography, in part because of its flexibility and

in part because Daguerre's process involved contact with mercury fumes that

could--and did--blind, and poison those working on the process.  Daguerre however

was the man in the limelight.  In the summer of 1839 Paris was consumed with

photography fever.  Amateur photographers reveled in cheap muddy prints of

buildings, crowds surged around the Institute of Science when the process was to be

described publicly, and bookstores could not keep Daguerre's manual in stock.  By

December the book was in its twenty-ninth edition and, photography mania had

become established throughout the western world. Few people know the names of

the men who invented photography, but for over one hundred fifty years we all have

enjoyed, the fruits of their discoveries.

## Exercise 14: Editing for Correct Use of Semicolons
### (*S & S* Handbook Chapter 25)

The following passage contains a number of errors in semicolon use: sometimes semicolons are used inappropriately, and sometimes other punctuation marks are used inappropriately in place of semicolons. Correct these errors, being careful to leave correct sentences as they are.

Vancouver, British Columbia is one of the most beautiful cities in North America. Looking out over the Strait of Georgia to Vancouver Island, the city boasts ultramodern buildings featuring offices, banks, and apartments, quaint marketplaces where vendors sell homemade foods, organically grown vegetables, and handmade crafts, and extensive parks designed for jogging, picnicking, and playing sports. One of the most fascinating attractions in Vancouver, however; is often overlooked. A trip to Vancouver can never be complete without a visit to the Museum of Anthropology at the University of British Columbia. Both inside and outside the imposing glass and concrete museum building, visitors can find objects from many cultures, including ancient African masks and huge native American totem poles. The totem poles are particularly fascinating; because they served many functions. Some were designed for the entryways to homes, others were constructed as memorials to the dead. On most of the totem poles, various combinations of three figures are used; humans, fish, and birds. While the poles themselves are both imposing and beautiful; it is even more interesting to learn why they were constructed as they were. The museum makes it easy to gain a basic understanding of the ancient art form by providing televisions through which visitors can watch a video explaining the meanings of various totem poles, making the artifacts even more fascinating to examine.

Regardless of whether visitors want to simply observe the mysterious artifacts, or to begin to understand their purpose; the Museum of Anthropology provides the perfect setting in which to become acquainted with a fascinating culture.

**Exercise 15: Editing for Correct Use of Colons**
(*S & S* Handbook Chapter 26)

**The following passage contains a number of errors in colon use: sometimes colons are used inappropriately, and sometimes other punctuation marks are used inappropriately in place of colons. Correct these errors, being careful to leave correct sentences as they are.**

It seems that the appearance of extraterrestrials is not something peculiar to the twentieth century. In the twelfth century: the residents of a village called Wulpet in England reported a very strange occurrence. While they were reaping one day, two children appeared from nearby caves. The appearance of strange children was unusual enough in this area, but these children were particularly unusual, they were green. Residents also claim that they wore clothes of strange color, made of materials unknown to anyone in the village. The children could not eat anything but beans when they first arrived, and told of a strange journey: they were playing in their land, where it was always twilight, and suddenly found themselves in the bright sunshine of Wulpet. They called their home St. Martin. Reports state: that the children eventually lost their green coloring and learned English. The boy died young, while the girl lived to be married. Apparently nobody followed her progress after her marriage: for nothing other than the original reports was ever written about them.

## Exercise 16:  Editing for Correct Use of Apostrophes
### (*S & S* Handbook Chapter 27)

**The following passage contains a number of errors in apostrophe use: sometimes apostrophes appear where they do not belong, and other times necessary apostrophes are missing.  Correct these errors.**

Ill always remember the "border wars" waged by my younger sister and me over our shared bedroom.  In our house, Kathy's and Patty's room was known as a military zone throughout our grade school and middle school years.  You see, I was a "neat freak."  Everything had to be in it's appointed place, and no dust or grime was tolerated.  Patty, on the other hand, didn't know the meaning of the word "neat."  Her bed was never made, her clothes were never hung up or put away, and her junk was always cluttering up our room.  My mother tried to settle thing's once by giving us a roll of white tape.  Patty and I were to divide the room in half by running the tape across the floor.  The right side of the room was mine, and the left side her's.  I could keep my side of the room as neat as I pleased, and Patty could revel in her filth without upsetting me.  In theory, of course, this should have worked.  But Mom had underestimated Pattys capacity to create messes.  Within weeks of the installation of the border, the junk had piled so high on her side of the room that it started spilling over into my territory.  Thus the border war began.  I was a crafty fighter, piling all of Pattys junk on top of her while she slept.  But she was a match for me.  While I was out, she would sneak into the room and carefully turn each of my treasured knicknacks on their heads.  Then she would switch my sock drawer with my pajama drawer.  These skirmishes would rage for weeks until we became tired enough to declare a truce--which usually lasted all of forty-eight hours before hostility's resumed.  Our parents attempts to solve the problem all failed.  You may wonder how we ever became close after all this fighting.  Actually, the solution had nothing to do with us.  Our older sister Mary, who had her own room, got married and moved out!

## Exercise 17:  Editing for Correct Use of Quotation Marks
### (*S & S* Handbook Chapter 28)

**The following passage contains a number of errors in the use of quotation marks and other punctuation with quotation marks:  Check for correct use of single and double quotation marks, for appropriate use of marks, and for placement of other punctuation with quotation marks.**

In preparing the class to read Nadine Gordimer's short story Some Monday for Sure, Ms. O'Brien asked us if anyone knew what the word 'apartheid' meant. Marilyn Nichols consulted a dictionary, which provided this definition:  any system or practice that separates people according to race, caste, etc.  The dictionary further explained that the word is an Afrikaans combination of apart and hood.  A discussion of the racial policies of the South African "government" followed.  Ms. O'Brien explained that the racial codes in South Africa forbid Black people from voting in general elections.  People who are neither white nor Black are referred to as colored, and vote in separate elections.  I asked, is this why there has been so much violent protest in that country?  "Skip" Solomon, who had been reading about South Africa in the newspapers, said that it was.  He also offered his opinion that "there would be a full-scale civil war if the situation continued."  "Your point is well taken", Ms. O'Brien stated, "because the rebels in "Some Monday for Sure" consider themselves to be in the midst of a civil war".

**Exercise 18:  Editing for Correct Use of Other Marks**
**(*S & S* Handbook Chapter 29)**

The following passage contains a number of errors in the use of
dashes, parentheses, brackets, ellipses, and slashes.  In some cases
the marks themselves are either misused or omitted; in other cases
other punctuation is used inappropriately with the marks.  Make
necessary corrections.


In 1984, the Planetary Society the world's largest space-interest organization

issued the Mars Declaration, urging the United States and the Soviet Union to join

forces to explore our nearest planetary neighbor, first with robots and finally with

human beings.  Signers of the declaration come from all walks of life, and represent

diverse political views, there are Republicans and Democrats on the list, as well as

liberals and conservatives.  Members of the society believe that if the U.S. and-or the

USSR can complete this mission, much can be gained, including better understanding

of the earth's climate and life forms.  As noted astronomer Carl Sagan puts the

question, "Is there something important on Mars that we need to know about our <u>own</u>

fragile planet (emphasis mine)?"  Perhaps even more exciting is the prospect of two

former enemies focusing their technology on a joint venture.  If military funds were to

be diverted from weapons to space exploration, claim supporters of the declaration,

the threat of nuclear war would be diminished substantially.  The Mars Declaration

enjoys a good deal of support, (both President Bush and Soviet President Gorbachev

have indicated support of the program), but it faces strong opposition from those who

feel that problems of hunger, homelessness, and a deteriorating environment on earth

must be met before more money is spent on space exploration. Of course, NASA the

National Aeronautics and Space Administration would very much like to see the program move forward.  Whether their wish will be granted remains to be seen.

However, when people think of the great explorations of the past, they

tend--Columbus' voyage to the New World, Magellan's circumnavigation of the

globe, Armstrong's walk on the moon--to look to that red spot in the sky, and think

that perhaps someday.

**Exercise 19:   Editing for Correct Use of Capitals, Italics, Abbreviations, Numbers (*S & S* Handbook Chapter 30)**

**The following paragraph contains a number or errors in the use of capitals, italics, abbreviations, and numbers.  Correct the errors (some forms are used correctly).**

In the south Pacific Ocean, 2300 mi. West of Chile, lies an island that has fascinated people for two and a half centuries.  Easter island, so named because it was discovered on Easter Sunday in seventeen twenty-two, has some strange inhabitants: about eight hundred stone figures, ranging in height from six to 33 ft,  stand guard atop huge stone platforms called  <u>ahu</u>s all along the coast of the island.  The statues have  huge heads, many of them sporting large  topknots called  pukao. Anthropologists have  traced these <u>Ahu Akivi</u>  statues back to the 10th century.  Some people believe that the statues were placed there by visitors from space, noting that many of the statues lie face-up on the ground, as if to communicate with traveling spacecraft.  But historians have discovered that when the Dutch explorers first found them, the figures were upright.  It was during Civil Wars on the island in the early eighteen hundreds that the statues were toppled.  Scientists who have studied the statues believe that they were built in honor of past Chiefs.  However, even with the question of their origin solved, one mystery remains:  How did the islanders, who had not yet invented the wheel, move statues of over 50 tons from the inland volcano where they were built to the coastal sites where they now stand?

**Exercise 20:** Editing for Correct Spelling and Hyphenation
(*S & S* Handbook Chapter 22)

**The following paragraph contains a number of errors in spelling and hyphenation. Correct the errors.**

In the past ten years the elephant population of Africa has been cut in half. Furthermore, some researchers beleive that by the turn of the century elephants will be almost extinct. What is the cause of this problem? Most researchers point to poaching, or illegaly slaughtering elephants for their tusks. The illegal ivory trade is an extremely-profitable business with a worldwide network of connections. Illegal ivory merchants hire poachers to slaughter elephants, often at night so that they are less likely to be detected. The tusks are buried untill they can be transported to a distribution point, usually a secret factory were the raw ivory is carved so that its origin cannot be discovered. The smugglers are protected throughout this process by corupt officials who except bribes from the powerful dealers. The carved ivory eventually finds its way to markets all over the world, many of them run by legitamate businessmen and women who think they are buying legal ivory. The problem has become so serious that conservationists are calling for a complete ban on ivory trade. They claim that the existance of restricted legal trade allows smugglers to steal and forge permits, as well as provideing them with access to legal markets. The only way to save the elephant from complete extinction, argue the conservationists, is to place them on the allinclusive indangered species list that prohibits any trade in there products. Ideally, conservationists would like to see the elephant population returned to its pre1979 level.

**Exercise 21:    Editing for Punctuation, Spelling, Hyphenation
(Summary Exercise)**

**The following paragraph contains a number of errors covered in
Exercises 13 through 20. Correct the errors.**

In 1926 a young woman of seventeen made her first trip to New York in order to

receive an award for one of her short-stories. That trip marked a turning point in the

life of Dorothy West, who went on to become one of the celebrated writer's of the

Harlem Renaissance. This group of black writers, poets, musicians, and painters,

brought national attention to Harlem in the 1920s, as they created works that

chronicled the lives of black Americans. West remembers the time as one of the most

exciting in her life, "We were young and hopeful. We all knew that we were going to

write the greatest story, paint the greatest picture. It was wonderful." Among the

writers West recalls working with are Zora Neale Hurston, author of "Their Eyes

Were Watching God, " Langston Hughes, who's poems Harlem and Epilogue are

still widely read, and Claude McKay, a jamaican immigrant who strongly influenced

West's writing. West shared an interest in alternative forms of government with

Hughes and other artists living in Harlem at the time, and in nineteen thirty-two she

joined them on a one year trip to the USSR. By the time she returned, the Harlem

Renaissance was in its death throes. The Depression was taking its toll on these

artists as it was on all Americans, and the desire to move on had caused many of the

writers to set out for Florida, California, and other new places. During the

Depression, West worked briefly for Franklin Delano Roosevelts WPA Works

Progress Administration before returning to her home in Boston. Many writers from the Harlem Renaissance, Langston Hughes, Countee Cullen, Wallace Thurman, and Zora Neale Hurston, to name a few, have since become established figures in American literature. West, however, was largly forgotten. Some of her short stories are still read, and she does readings at colleges in the Boston area, but she spends most of her time writting for a small newspaper on Martha's Vineyard, an island off the coast of Cape Cod, Mass. The literary world has not heard the last of Dorothy West, however. At the age of eighty, she is hard at work on a new novel. The Harlem Renaissance as a movement may be over, but its influence on American Literature promises to remain strong.

## Part VI

**REVISING AND EDITING PARAGRAPHS**
          (Summary Exercises for Parts III, IV, V)


The following paragraphs contain errors that have been covered in Parts III, IV, and V of this workbook. Revise and edit each paragraph, first making appropriate corrections in the paragraph itself, and then copying the revised and edited paragraph on a separate sheet of paper.

**Exercise 22:**

If you want to get a real sense of what it was like to live in New England in the early years of the British settlements, visit the town of Plymouth, Massachusetts. You will find yourself entering a world that has been dead for almost four hundred years. As you step onto the deck of the Mayflower. You may be greeted by a sailor expressing confusion at the sight of women in pants. If you ask him his views on nuclear energy; he will respond with a blank stare. But ask him about the voyage across the Atlantic and he becomes excited, proudly telling you how he and his mates kept the ship afloat and many of the passengers alive during the treacherous journey. Below decks, some of the passengers will tell you of nights spent huddled together to keep warm, that many people died during the crossing, and of the births as well. Down the road at Plimoth Plantation, you can walk into the house of one of the settlers and talk with the housewife prepareing dinner over an open hearth. She will warn you that frequent bathing brings on disease and she will look scandalized if you ask her why she does not insist that her husband help out with the household chores. The world of the inhabitant's, interpreters is actually what they're called, of the Mayflower and Plimoth Plantation is the world of the sixteen twenties; they know nothing of events that happened after there time on earth. But they know almost everything about life in early New England, and once the visitor overcomes their initial shyness about conversing with people from another time, they can learn more than any book will tell them about the people who founded this colony.

**Exercise 23:**

Some people think of summer camp as a place where children learn to swim, ride, play tennis, sail, and do crafts. But there is a very special summer camp that teaches young people (teenagers in this case) far more than how to make potholders and tie knots. Anytown, the name of the camp, does not have a single location, instead it is a program that can be run in any part of the country. The camp brings together teenagers of diverse backgrounds, and it fosters understanding among races, cultures, and religions. The concept for Anytown began in 1959 in Phoenix, Ariz. Now there are twelve Anytown camps across the country, some in large cities, others in small towns. Anytown campers represent the leaders in schools and community and religious organizations. They are recommended by teachers or officers of the organizations, and the schools and organizations usually cough up the bucks for the students to attend. While campers do many of the things ordinary campers do, swimming, sports, art, they spend most of their time in discussion groups and workshops that help them understand different races, cultures, and religions. Social issues such as abortion, police community relations, and disabilities are also discussed. Guest speakers include people which are prominent in the community, and often those who can attest to the problems caused by intolerance. At one Anytown camp, a survivor of the Holocaust is speaking to students about her experiences in Nazi concentration camps. One of the most difficult, but enlightening, features of Anytown takes place on the day that students are told that they can only associate with members of their own group. The camp director acts as a dictator, enforcing segregation. Since this day is always held toward the end of the two week period, students of different backgrounds all ready have become friends. As a result of this experiment in segregating and separating people of different races, cultures, and religions that the campers all take part and participate in during the particular day in question, they realize how difficult it is to live in a social system that does not allow them to choose friends freely. Most students hate the separation day, but they also realize how valuable it is in encouraging them to fight prejudice and intolerance. When they leave Anytown, campers realize that everyone is special, and differences are just that--differences, nothing more. As one camper put it, 'If everyone spent two weeks at Anytown, there would be no prejudice or intolerance left in the world.'

**Exercise 24:**

Before the civil war the United States was primarily a rural country, a nation of farmers. American literature reflected that reality;   Washington Irving wrote eloquently about life in the Hudson River Valley, and Mark Twain created adventures along the banks of the Mississippi River for Tom Sawyer and Huckleberry Finn. Such writers as them rarely chose the city for their setting; the real life of the United States took place in small towns,  rural areas, and where the wilderness was untamed. However, the American landscape began to change drastically toward the end of the nineteenth century.  With the rise of industrialism, many poor farmers gave up their rural life to move to the city and work in factories.  Freed slaves also found their way to northern cities in hopes of taking part in the American dream.  Along with the farmers and slaves immigrants  from all over Europe poured into New York, Boston, Chicago, and other cities.  By 1900 the populations of the nations  major cities had grown substantially, and ethnic neighborhoods became little cities within the larger metropolis.  During the early part of the 20th  century the neighborhoods in which factory workers lived became overcrowded and run down, and as developers ran out of land in the business districts, buildings became taller and taller.  Casting  a shadow over once bright, pleasant landscapes.  With these changes that were just previously mentioned,  the literature of the nation changed as well.  Now writers began to turn their attention from the wide open spaces to the congested streets of the city.  And the picture they presented was not pleasant. Stephen Crane, for example, showed his readers the horrifying human cost of poverty in the slums of New York City in his short novel "Maggie, A Girl of the Streets."  And Upton Sinclair, in his novel "The

Octopus," exposed the corruption of the Chicago meat-packing industry. Similarly,

Edith Wharton revealed the moral emptiness of New York's high society in such

novels as "The House of Mirth."  With the clearly visible injustices that accompanied

the urbanization of America, the country's literature changed from romantic tails  of

good triumphing over evil to realistic stories of people who, because of their poverty,

was enslaved by the wealthy people who ruled the cities.